10 TRUTHS
about your identity
in Christ that will
transform your life.

30 DAY WORKBOOK/ DEVOTIONAL

ReBorn
A New Identity

BOLA OLIVIA OGEDENGBE

Beautiful Books

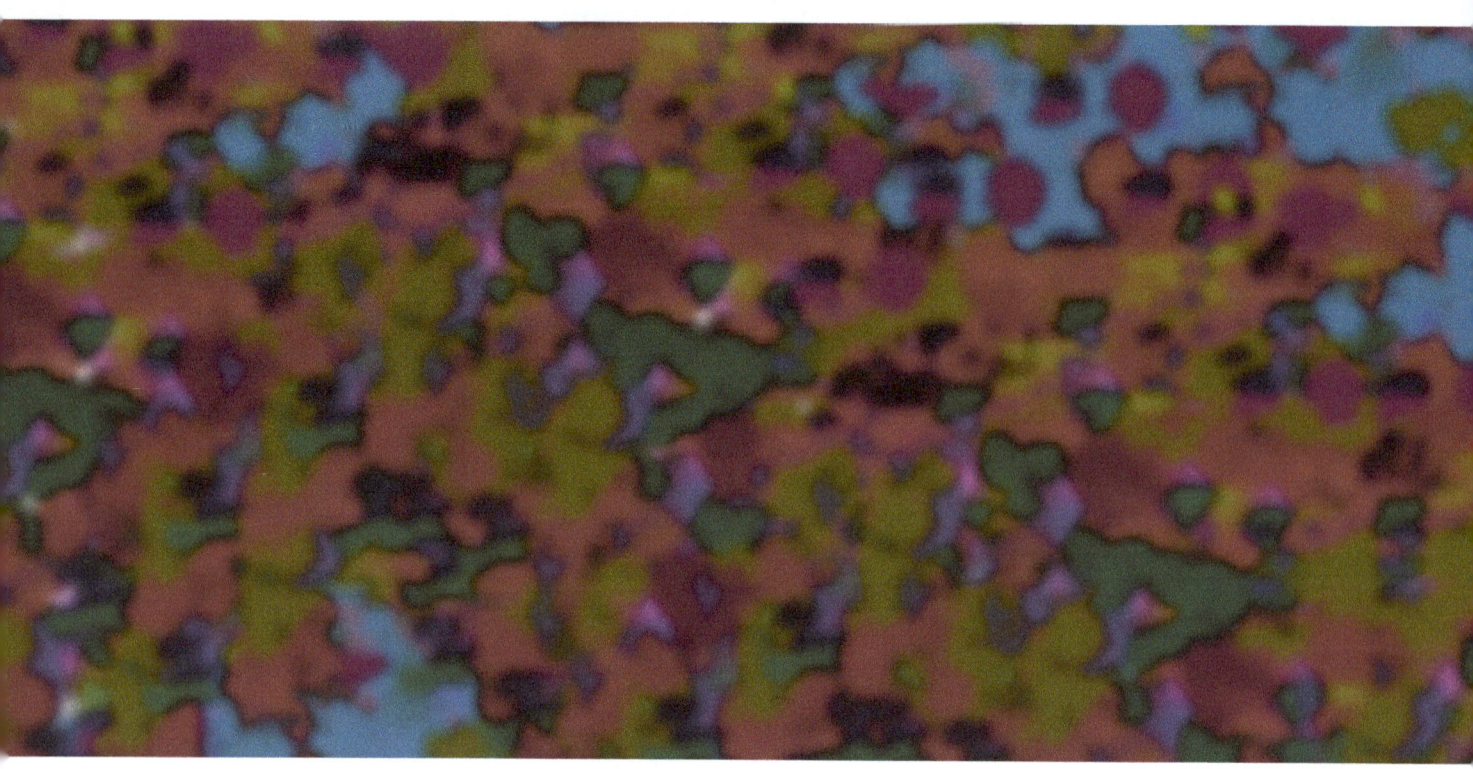

REBORN A New Identity Companion Workbook
Copyright © 2017 Bolanle Ogedengbe

All rights reserved. No part of this publication may be reproduced, stored in a retrieval system, distributed, or transmitted in any form or by any means, including photocopying, recording, or other electronic or mechanical methods, except for brief quotations in printed reviews, without the prior written permission of the publisher.

ISBN 979-10-95039-06-8   9791095039068

All Scripture quotations, unless otherwise indicated, are taken from The Holy Bible, New International Version® NIV®. Copyright © 1973, 1978, 1984 by International Bible Society®. Used by permission.

Printed in the United Kingdom

Dedication

This book is dedicated to all the men and women I have had the privilege of teaching over the past twenty years. Your hunger for the Word of God and desire to learn have helped make me the teacher that I am.

May you continue to grow in grace, and in your love for the Master.

TABLE of CONTENTS

Foreword..4

Days 1-3 (Born Of God)..5

Days 4-6 (Loved Of God Loving God) 17

Days 7-9 (Adopted Into God's Family)..............................29

Days 10-12 (Forgiven)..41

Days 13-15 (Declared Not Guilty)..................................53

Days 16-18 (Indwelt by the Holy Spirit) 65

Days 19-21 (Delivered, Invested With Authority)................77

Days 22-24 (Delivered From Sickness)..............................89

Days 25-27 (Fully Provided For)....................................101

Days 28-30 (Kingdom Citizen & Ambassador)..................113

Conclusion..125

FOREWORD

Many years ago, a dear friend made this statement, 'It is a wonderful life in Christ.' I did not understand it because I was not 'in Christ'. Sometime later I came to faith in Christ and to the understanding of what it is to be 'in Christ'. Then began a journey of discovering the richness of the new identity of a born again child of God. That is the subject of REBORN A New Identity.

This workbook covers each chapter of the book, the ten dimensions of this new identity. It includes quotes, Scriptures, prayers, a call to action and notes. It is a primer and a foundation. It can be used alone or preferably in conjunction with the book to fully benefit from all the content and exercises in the book itself.

Everyday, read or reread the chapter for the day, meditate on the Scriptures in the Workbook, then answer the questions for the day and say the prayers. Everyday, take time to write in the Notes section.

May you be filled with insight, wisdom and revelation. Shalom!

BORN of GOD

Everyone who believes that Jesus is the Christ is born of God, and everyone who loves the father loves his child as well.
1 John 5.1

QUOTES

THE HOLY SPIRIT MAKES OUR SPIRIT ALIVE, AND IT IS NO LONGER SEPARATED FROM GOD BECAUSE OF SIN.

First, the birth by which we gained physical entrance into this natural world. That is what Jesus called being born of the flesh.

Then there is the second birth by which we gain spiritual entrance into the supernatural world of God. Jesus called it being born of the Spirit. That is the new birth experience.

You are now born of God. You are no longer 'dead in your sins'. Your outward appearance may be the same, but make no mistake—you are what the Book calls 'a new creation'.

You have been transferred from the dominion of darkness into the kingdom of God. You are now a child of light.

SCRIPTURES

"In reply Jesus declared, "I tell you the truth, no-one can see the kingdom of God unless he is born again." (John 3.3)

"Everyone who believes that Jesus is the Christ is born of God."
(1 John 5.1a)

"Therefore, if anyone is in Christ, he is a new creation; the old has gone, the new has come!"
(2 Corinthians 5.17)

"But these are written that you may believe that Jesus is the Christ, the Son of God, and that by believing you may have life in his name."
(John 20.31)

"And this is the testimony: God has given us eternal life, and this life is in his Son. He who has the Son has life; he who does not have the Son of God does not have life." (1 John 5.11-12)

DAY 1

QUESTIONS:

The book discusses Jesus' conversation with Nicodemus. Can you explain what He told him?

How is a person born of God?

DAY 1

PRAYER: Thanksgiving

Thank God for the new birth in Christ Jesus.

Thank God that the life of God is in you now.

OTHER PRAYER POINTS

NOTES

What impact has this study had on you? Note other lessons you have learnt from the study.

DAY 2

QUESTIONS:

Read 1 John 5.11-12.
Explain the implications of this Scripture.

Explain the phrase 'eternal life'. How does it apply to you?

DAY 2

PRAYER: Thanksgiving

Thank God for saving you from an eternity in hell and giving you the hope of heaven.

Thank God for transferring you into the kingdom of Jesus.

OTHER PRAYER POINTS

NOTES

What impact has this study had on you? Note other lessons you have learnt from the study.

DAY 3

QUESTIONS:

Read John 3.18.
What does this mean for you now that you believe?

Page 17 talks about 'eternal destination'. What does that mean for you?

DAY 3

PRAYER: Petition

Ask God to bless you by making your life useful for His kingdom.

Ask Him to teach you everything you need to take His Word of salvation to your generation.

OTHER PRAYER POINTS

NOTES

What impact has this study had on you? Note other lessons you have learnt from the study.

2

LOVED of GOD
and LOVING GOD

We love because he first loved us.

1 John 4.19

Days 4-6

QUOTES

GOD'S LOVE FOR US IS ONE OF THE MOST CONSISTENT TESTIMONIES OF SCRIPTURE. IT IS A DEEP, UNQUALIFIED, OVERRIDING LOVE WHEREBY HE EVER SEEKS TO DO US GOOD.

Many people fear coming to God because they think He cannot love them because of their wickedness. The father in this story could not wait to take his son in his arms. In his eagerness, he ran towards him. What an amazing picture of love.

Loving God enables you to have a beautiful relationship with Him, to enjoy Him and He you. And this love will continue to grow as you spend time with Him in prayer and read His Word.

You can no longer be self-seeking and thinking only of what suits you. You will now be looking for ways to please God.

SCRIPTURES

 *"Jesus replied: "Love the Lord your God with all your heart and with all your soul and with all your mind." (Matthew 22.37)*

"This is love for God: to obey his commands. And his commands are not burdensome." (1 John 5.3)

"But God demonstrates his own love for us in this: While we were still sinners, Christ died for us." (Romans 5.8)

"And we know that in all things God works for the good of those who love him, who have been called according to his purpose." (Romans 8.28)

"Though you have not seen him, you love him; and even though you do not see him now, you believe in him and are filled with an inexpressible and glorious joy, for you are receiving the goal of your faith, the salvation of your souls." (1 Peter 1.8-9)

DAY 4

QUESTIONS:

In what way does the story told by Jesus illustrate the love of God for humanity?

Read Romans 5.8.

What dimension of God's love is shown here?

DAY 4

PRAYER: Thanksgiving

Thank God for His unending love. Be specific about the expressions of that love.

Thank God for giving you the capacity to love Him.

OTHER PRAYER POINTS

NOTES

What impact has this study had on you? Note other lessons you have learnt from the study.

DAY 5

QUESTIONS:

Read 1 John 4.9-11.
How does this passage explain the meaning of love?

What is the conclusion drawn in the above passage and how do you apply it to your life?

DAY 5

PRAYER: Petition

Ask that you will come to fully understand the implications of being loved by God.

Pray that you will be consumed with love for God.

OTHER PRAYER POINTS

NOTES

What impact has this study had on you? Note other lessons you have learnt from the study.

DAY 6

QUESTIONS:

What does it mean to love the Lord with all your heart, all your soul and all your mind?

"It is a wonderful thing to love God, to have your affections directed at the Almighty Himself." (Page 28). Explain.

DAY 6

PRAYER: Petition

Pray against disobedience in your life. Commit to obey God and ask that all rebellion be destroyed in your life.

Pray that you will enjoy the fruits of loving God, enumerate them in your prayer as they are explained in the book.

OTHER PRAYER POINTS

NOTES

What impact has this study had on you? Note other lessons you have learnt from the study.

Adopted
into
God's Family

3

How great is the love the Father has lavished on us, that we should be called children of God! And that is what we are! The reason the world does not know us is that it did not know him.
1 John 3.1

Days 7-9

QUOTES

WHEN YOU CAME TO FAITH IN CHRIST JESUS, GOD LITERALLY ADOPTED YOU INTO HIS FAMILY.

Every child of God needs to have a deep understanding of God as their own Father, not simply as the Father of humanity as a whole, but their own Father.

Whatever your image of a father is, let God change your thinking so that it will not hinder you from enjoying this beautiful father/child relationship with your heavenly Father.

A Father who is faithful, a Father who protects, who liberates His people from bondage, from fear, and from insecurity. He is a Father who makes full provision for His own, and never abandons them.

Jesus is the unique Son of God. And He came to the earth so that we can also become sons of God.

SCRIPTURES

"Yet to all who received him, to those who believed in his name, he gave the right to become children of God." (John 1.12)

"For you did not receive a spirit that makes you a slave again to fear, but you received the Spirit of sonship. And by him we cry, "Abba, Father." The Spirit himself testifies with our spirit that we are God's children." (Romans 8.15-16)

"You are all sons of God through faith in Christ Jesus." (Galatians 3.26)

"Now if we are children, then we are heirs - heirs of God and co-heirs with Christ, if indeed we share in his sufferings in order that we may also share in his glory." (Romans 8.17)

DAY 7

QUESTIONS:

Note some of the lessons learnt about divine adoption from the explanation given in the passage.

Read Romans 8.15-16. Who is the Spirit of sonship and what role does He play in your life?

DAY 7

PRAYER: Thanksgiving

Thank God for adopting you into His family. Tell Him how you feel about it.

Praise God for the Spirit of sonship and begin to do what the Bible says He helps us to do.

OTHER PRAYER POINTS

NOTES

What impact has this study had on you? Note other lessons you have learnt from the study.

DAY 8

QUESTIONS:

So you are an heir of God. What does that mean and what difference does it make for you?

From the explanation given, in your view what kind of father is God?

DAY 8

PRAYER:

Ask for a deep understanding of divine adoption.

Pray a prayer of submission, to submit yourself completely to your heavenly Father.

OTHER PRAYER POINTS

NOTES

What impact has this study had on you? Note other lessons you have learnt from the study.

DAY 9

QUESTIONS:

Read Isaiah 46.4. What is the connection between this passage (Page 40) and being adopted by God?

What do we learn about divine protection in relation to sonship. What difference does it make for you?

DAY 9

PRAYER: Petition

Pray that your life will always honour your heavenly Father who has loved you so much.

Pray for divine guidance and protection.

OTHER PRAYER POINTS

NOTES

What impact has this study had on you? Note other lessons you have learnt from the study.

FORGIVEN

4

For he has rescued us from the dominion of darkness and brought us into the kingdom of the Son he loves, in whom we have redemption, the forgiveness of sins.
Col. 1.13-14

Days 10-12

QUOTES

THE ONE PERSON AUTHORIZED TO HOLD A SWORD OF DAMOCLES OVER YOUR HEAD HAS CHOSEN NOT TO.

That is one of the reasons why Jesus came, so that God will have legal grounds for forgiving us.

God is infinitely rich in grace and He has poured forgiveness out in the measure of that richness of grace. It is rich grace of unlimited quantity and quality.

Do not fall into the trap of self condemnation, rather, forgive yourself and glorify God for His kindness to you. God has forgiven you and He offers you a new beginning.

The truth is that people are already guilty, and as they draw nearer to God, they become more conscious of their guilt. But God wants to free them from it.

SCRIPTURES

"I, even I, am he who blots out your transgressions, for my own sake, and remembers your sins no more."
(Isaiah 43.25)

"For he has rescued us from the dominion of darkness and brought us into the kingdom of the Son he loves, in whom we have redemption, the forgiveness of sins."
(Colossians 1.13-14)

"Their sins and lawless acts I will remember no more."
(Hebrews 10.17)

"This is my blood of the covenant, which is poured out for many for the forgiveness of sins."
(Matthew 26.28)

"This is love for God: to obey his commands. And his commands are not burdensome."
(1 John 5.3)

"In him we have redemption through his blood, the forgiveness of sins, in accordance with the riches of God's grace." (Ephesians 1.7)

DAY 10

QUESTIONS:

Based on the story of the repentant thief, how is forgiveness granted? What else does one learn from Jesus' treatment of the man?

Note your conclusions on the story of the composer of 'Amazing Grace' as told in the book.

DAY 10

PRAYER: Thanksgiving

Confess any known sin. Thank God for forgiveness of sins.

Thank Jesus for what He went through to save you.

OTHER PRAYER POINTS

NOTES

What impact has this study had on you? Note other lessons you have learnt from the study.

DAY 11

QUESTIONS:

On page 49 there is a story about forgiveness being 'easy'. What is your perspective?

If God will forgive someone at the last minute, why should anyone receive forgiveness now rather than wait till later?

DAY 11

PRAYER:

Ask for understanding of the cost of your free forgiveness.

Pray for a grateful heart.

OTHER PRAYER POINTS

NOTES

What impact has this study had on you? Note other lessons you have learnt from the study.

DAY 12

QUESTIONS:

Why did Jesus have to die for us to be forgiven?

God does not remember our sins when we repent. What does this mean for you and how do you respond to it?

DAY 12

PRAYER: Petition

Pray and forgive yourself for past mistakes.

Commit to walking right before God. Ask God to redeem the wasted years.

OTHER PRAYER POINTS

NOTES

What impact has this study had on you? Note other lessons you have learnt from the study.

Declared NOT GUILTY

For all have sinned and fall short of the glory of God, and are justified freely by his grace through the redemption that came by Christ Jesus.

Romans 3.23-24

5

Days 13-15

QUOTES

YOU ARE NOT JUST FORGIVEN, YOU HAVE ALSO BEEN DECLARED NOT GUILTY. THE CHARGES AGAINST YOU HAVE BEEN DROPPED.

When they ask why you have changed your lifestyle, tell them it is because God wiped out your sins, gave you a clean garment and you want to keep it clean.

Jesus carried the weight and penalty of sins He did not commit, so we can be put in a right relationship with God which we do not deserve.

In redemption, Jesus paid the price for humans to be released from the captivity of sin and from the penalty of sin. That price is the reason that, because of the kindness of God, we can be declared just.

Stop flirting with sin. Some things you used to do are no longer worthy of you. You are now a new creation.

SCRIPTURES

 *"The next day John saw Jesus coming towards him and said, "Look, the Lamb of God who takes away the sin of the world!"*
(John 1.29)

"For we know that our old self was crucified with him so that the body of sin might be done away with, that we should no longer be slaves to sin...In the same way count yourselves dead to sin, but alive to God in Christ Jesus."
(Romans 6.6,11)

"I have been crucified with Christ and I no longer live, but Christ lives in me."
(Galatians 2.20a)

"...and are justified freely by his grace through the redemption that came by Christ Jesus."
(Romans 3.24)

DAY 13

QUESTIONS:

The story of Jason is vivid and powerful. What are the lessons that you have taken away from it? (P60)

What is your understanding of, and response to the divine exchange?

DAY 13

PRAYER: Thanksgiving

Thank God for forgiveness and for wiping the slate clean. Spend some time blessing Him for this.

Thank God for giving you a new identity. Thank Him for setting you free from condemnation.

OTHER PRAYER POINTS

NOTES

What impact has this study had on you? Note other lessons you have learnt from the study.

DAY 14

QUESTIONS:

What difference does it make to you that you have been declared not guilty?

Jesus won victory over sin. How is His victory over sin your victory over sin?

DAY 14

PRAYER:

Pray for revelation of the full dimension of this truth, that you are no longer considered guilty.

Ask to be delivered from every form of bondage and also residual condemnation and guilt.

OTHER PRAYER POINTS

NOTES

What impact has this study had on you? Note other lessons you have learnt from the study.

DAY 15

QUESTIONS:

Read 1 Cor 6.19-20. What are the four things it says about you and how to live now?

Can you explain in detail what the Bible means by honouring God with your body?

DAY 15

PRAYER: Petition

Renounce sin. Pray a prayer of commitment to change your lifestyle and keep your garment clean.

Pray seriously that God will give you a heart that hungers for and finds joy in holiness and purity.

OTHER PRAYER POINTS

NOTES

What impact has this study had on you? Note other lessons you have learnt from the study.

Indwelt by the HOLY SPIRIT

And I will ask the Father, and he will give you another Counsellor to be with you forever— the Spirit of truth. The world cannot accept him, because it neither sees him nor knows him. But you know him, for he lives with you and will be in you.
John 14.16-17

Days 16-18

QUOTES

THE HOLY SPIRIT IS THE THIRD PERSON OF THE TRINITY, THUS A PERSON WHO ACTS, THINKS, SPEAKS AND EXPRESSES VOLITION, NOT AN IMPERSONAL FORCE.

When Jesus speaks of the other Comforter to come, He is not speaking of any other prophet coming after Him, but of God the Holy Spirit, who did indeed come on the day of Pentecost.

The Spirit knows the mind of the Father and will show you the direction to take in life and what to think, say or do. As you follow Him, your life will naturally fulfil divine purpose.

Isn't it remarkable that the last conversation Jesus had with His disciples on the earth had to do with the Holy Spirit?

SCRIPTURES

 *"But the Counsellor, the Holy Spirit, whom the Father will send in my name, will teach you all things and will remind you of everything I have said to you." (John 14.26)*

"If you love me, you will obey what I command. And I will ask the Father, and he will give you another Counsellor to be with you for ever—the Spirit of truth. The world cannot accept him, because it neither sees him nor knows him. But you know him, for he lives with you and will be in you." (John 14.15-17)

"Do you not know that your body is a temple of the Holy Spirit, who is in you, whom you have received from God? You are not your own." (1 Corinthians 6.19)

"In the same way, the Spirit helps us in our weakness. We do not know what we ought to pray for, but the Spirit himself intercedes for us with groans that words cannot express." (Romans 8.26)

DAY 16

QUESTIONS:

What lesson do you draw from the short story of Philip about your relationship with the Holy Spirit?

Based on John 14.15-17 and the explanation following it on page 70, who is the Holy Spirit?

DAY 16

PRAYER: Thanksgiving

Thank the Father for the gift of the Holy Spirit.

Spend time praising God for His great love in not only giving us His Son but also giving us His Spirit.

CONFESSION

I am filled with the Holy Spirit. He teaches me to pray according to the heart of the Father.
My body is the temple of the Holy Spirit. I live a pure and holy life.

NOTES

What impact has this study had on you? Note other lessons you have learnt from the study.

DAY 17

QUESTIONS:

Discuss four of the eleven actions of the Holy Spirit.

List the remaining seven.

DAY 17

PRAYER:

Pray for deeper revelation of, and intimacy with the Holy Spirit.

Invite the Holy Spirit to operate in your life, listing the different actions of the Holy Spirit.

OTHER CONFESSIONS

NOTES

What impact has this study had on you? Note other lessons you have learnt from the study.

DAY 18

QUESTIONS:

What is the baptism of the Holy Spirit and how does one receive it?

List some of the benefits of praying in tongues.

DAY 18

PRAYER: Petition

Pray to be baptized in the Holy Spirit.

Spend time worshipping the Lord by the Spirit.

OTHER CONFESSIONS

NOTES

What impact has this study had on you? Note other lessons you have learnt from the study.

7

Delivered
Invested with
Authority

And having disarmed the powers and authorities, he made a public spectacle of them, triumphing over them by the cross.

Colossians 2.15

Days 19-21

QUOTES

THE TIDE TURNED WHEN JESUS DEFEATED THE DEVIL ON THE CROSS, AND SUCCEEDED IN HIS AVOWED INTENTION OF DESTROYING THE WORKS OF THE DEVIL.

So all demonic forces are totally, irrevocably and forever subject to Him. The Scriptures add that every believer is in like position as Jesus; seated spiritually in the heavenly places.

We have to contend with a sophisticated command structure of spiritual forces of darkness. And they use different means of attack - temptation to sin, oppression, possession, sickness, etc.

Human responsibility cannot be denied, but humans are strongly influenced and sometimes compelled by the devil to do evil; and do themselves suffer evil.

Satan has lost every right to oppress you. You have gained full rights to stop his attacks every time. If you will boldly stand up to him and rebuke him, he is compelled to leave you alone.

SCRIPTURES

"Be self-controlled and alert. Your enemy the devil prowls around like a roaring lion looking for someone to devour."
(1 Peter 5.8)

"He who does what is sinful is of the devil, because the devil has been sinning from the beginning. The reason the Son of God appeared was to destroy the devil's work."
(1 John 3.8)

"Submit yourselves, then, to God. Resist the devil, and he will flee from you."
(James 4.7)

"And having disarmed the powers and authorities, he made a public spectacle of them, triumphing over them by the cross."
(Colossians 2.15)

"I have given you authority to trample on snakes and scorpions and to overcome all the power of the enemy; nothing will harm you."
(Luke 10.19)

DAY 19

QUESTIONS:

What is your reaction to the author's story? In what areas are your experiences similar or different?

Read 1 Peter 5.8. In what way does this improve your understanding of the activities of the devil?

DAY 19

PRAYER: Thanksgiving

Thank God for opening your eyes to know the truth of spiritual realities.

Thank God for freedom from the devil's devouring as stated in 1 Peter 5.8.

OTHER PRAYER POINTS

NOTES

What impact has this study had on you? Note other lessons you have learnt from the study.

DAY 20

QUESTIONS:

Explain some of the devil's forms of attack.

How do demons gain access to people?

DAY 20

PRAYER:

Pray for revelation of the victory of Jesus over the devil.

Renounce the devil and every work of darkness you were involved with before.

OTHER PRAYER POINTS

NOTES

What impact has this study had on you? Note other lessons you have learnt from the study.

DAY 21

QUESTIONS:

What did Jesus do in relation to the devil?

What is the position of Jesus now in relation to the devil and how does that affect your life?

DAY 21

PRAYER: Petition

Pray to be totally free of every demonic influence, and to be healed of any sickness caused by demons.

Pray for total restoration of all that the devil has stolen from you.

OTHER PRAYER POINTS

NOTES

What impact has this study had on you? Note other lessons you have learnt from the study.

Delivered from
SICKNESS

8

When evening came, many who were demon-possessed were brought to him, and he drove out the spirits with a word and healed all the sick. This was to fulfil what was spoken through the prophet Isaiah: "He took up our infirmities and carried our diseases."

Matthew 8.16-17

Days 22-24

QUOTES

HEALING IS GOD DOING GOOD. AND EVERYWHERE THAT JESUS WENT HE DID GOOD AND HEALED ALL THE OPPRESSED.

Unlike ritual laws that change from the Old to the New Testament, healing as the expressed will of God to bless His people remains the same.

Healing is the expression of the will of God.

God has always healed; it is part of His nature to heal. Do you know that God has names? I know, you probably thought His name was God. Well, one of God's names is Jehovah Rophe - the Lord who heals.

Disobedience brings sickness. It is not, however the sole cause of sickness as we live in a broken world where evil dominates.

SCRIPTURES

 *"He himself bore our sins in his body on the tree, so that we might die to sins and live for righteousness; by his wounds you have been healed."*
(1 Peter 2.24)

"When evening came, many who were demon-possessed were brought to him, and he drove out the spirits with a word and healed all the sick. This was to fulfil what was spoken through the prophet Isaiah: "He took up our infirmities and carried our diseases." (Matthew 8.16-17)

"Surely he took up our infirmities and carried our sorrows, yet we considered him stricken by God, smitten by him, and afflicted. But he was pierced for our transgressions, he was crushed for our iniquities; the punishment that brought us peace was upon him, and by his wounds we are healed."
(Isaiah 53.4-5)

DAY 22

QUESTIONS:

What is your impression of what happened in Peter's home after his mother-in-law was healed?

Why is that event significant?

DAY 22

PRAYER: Thanksgiving

Thank God for His goodness and provision for your healing.

Thank God for Jesus' sacrifice that makes healing accessible for us.

CONFESSIONS

By the stripes that wounded the Lord Jesus, I was healed and made whole.
I thank God for divine healing, I am strong and not weak, healthy and not sick, in Jesus' name.

NOTES

What impact has this study had on you? Note other lessons you have learnt from the study.

DAY 23

QUESTIONS:

What about the apostles? What does their experience with healing teach us?

Why did God heal?

DAY 23

PRAYER:

Ask for revelation of the truths of divine healing.

Pray for healing for your own body.

OTHER PRAYER POINTS

NOTES

What impact has this study had on you? Note other lessons you have learnt from the study.

DAY 24

QUESTIONS:

Does God still heal today?

How does healing come?

DAY 24

PRAYER: Petition

Pray for the healing of your loved ones.

Praise God for your healing.

OTHER PRAYER POINTS

NOTES

What impact has this study had on you? Note other lessons you have learnt from the study.

9

fully provided *for*

If you, then, though you are evil, know how to give good gifts to your children, how much more will your Father in heaven give good gifts to those who ask him!

Matthew 7.11

Days 25-27

QUOTES

JESUS TOLD US TO ASK THE FATHER TO PROVIDE FOR US BECAUSE HE KNOWS THAT HE CAN AND WILL DO IT.

Born again believers now have a Father in heaven, One who, like Jesus in this story, is compassionate. One who knows, and intends to meet the needs of His own children even before they ask. Jesus taught His disciples to address God as Father, and to ask Him, quite boldly, "Give us this day our daily bread."

You can stop worrying about the future and about material things. Remember that Jesus specifically told us that it is those who have no God who worry about such things.

Your generosity will bless others and yourself as well. The book of James shows us that some do not receive from God because of their selfishness.

Jesus who is the perfect expression of God expressly states that God's people are not to worry about material things such as food, clothes and shoes, as their Father in heaven already knows that they need these things.

SCRIPTURES

"Keep your lives free from the love of money and be content with what you have, because God has said, "Never will I leave you; never will I forsake you." (Hebrews 13.5)

"Look at the birds of the air; they do not sow or reap or store away in barns, and yet your heavenly Father feeds them. Are you not much more valuable than they...So do not worry, saying, 'What shall we eat?' or 'What shall we drink?' or 'What shall we wear?' For the pagans run after all these things, and your heavenly Father knows that you need them. But seek first his kingdom and his righteousness, and all these things will be given to you as well." (Matthew 6.26, 31-33)

"And my God will meet all your needs according to His glorious riches in Christ Jesus."
(Philippians 4.19)

"O LORD our God, as for all this abundance that we have provided for building you a temple for your Holy Name, it comes from your hand, and all of it belongs to you."
(1 Chronicles 29.16)

DAY 25

QUESTIONS:

The chapter begins with the story of the miraculous feeding of the multitude. In what way were love and compassion satisfied through this miracle?

What is the connection between the new birth and enjoying provision from God?

DAY 25

PRAYER: Thanksgiving

Thank God for the promise of divine provision.

Thank God for all the things you will no longer need to worry about. List them.

CONFESSIONS

I am blessed of God. The Lord is my provider and I am free of lack.
I am free of worry, anxiety and doubt.

NOTES

What impact has this study had on you? Note other lessons you have learnt from the study.

DAY 26

QUESTIONS:

What did Jesus say about our attitude to material things?

How did He teach us to pray in connection with our needs?

DAY 26

PRAYER:

Ask God for understanding of His financial system.

Commit to seek first His kingdom as Jesus said, and ask Him to help you to do this.

OTHER PRAYER POINTS

NOTES

What impact has this study had on you? Note other lessons you have learnt from the study.

DAY 27

QUESTIONS:

Is there anything that can stop us from receiving provision from God?

Read Hebrews 13.5. What is your perspective on this Scripture?

DAY 27

PRAYER: Petition

Renounce selfishness and the love of money, ask for a generous spirit.

Ask the Lord for provision for the specific needs in your life.

OTHER PRAYER POINTS

NOTES

What impact has this study had on you? Note other lessons you have learnt from the study.

kingdom citizen, AMBASSADOR

10

For the kingdom of God is not a matter of eating and drinking, but of righteousness, peace, and joy in the Holy Spirit. Romans 14.17

"We are therefore Christ's ambassadors, as though God were making his appeal through us. We implore you on Christ's behalf: Be reconciled to God."
2 Corinthians 5.20

Days 28-30

QUOTES

YOU HAVE BEEN GIVEN THE RESPONSIBILITY OF CONNECTING OTHERS TO GOD, OF RECONCILING PEOPLE TO GOD AS YOU WERE RECONCILED.

A new era had begun, an era of the reign of God, the dominion of God, and it began with His ministry and subsequent death and resurrection, which opened the way for others to enter the kingdom through repentance and faith in Jesus.

You are an official representative of Christ on earth. The Lord, as Paul puts it, makes His appeal through you. And your cry to them is, 'Be reconciled to God'.

The kingdom of God is that treasure, that pearl that is so infinitely precious that we will exchange all that we own for it.

As an ambassador of God's kingdom, your lifestyle must be worthy of God, and you must work for the interests of His kingdom and His church on the earth. Put away habits and plans that make you unfruitful for God.

SCRIPTURES

"We are therefore Christ's ambassadors, as though God were making his appeal through us. We implore you on Christ's behalf: Be reconciled to God."
(2 Corinthians 5.20)

"So do not worry, saying, 'What shall we eat?' or 'What shall we drink?' or 'What shall we wear?' For the pagans run after all these things, and your heavenly Father knows that you need them. But seek first his kingdom and his righteousness, and all these things will be given to you as well."
(Matthew 6.31-33)

"Do you not know that the wicked will not inherit the kingdom of God? Do not be deceived: Neither the sexually immoral, nor idolaters, nor adulterers, nor male prostitutes nor homosexual offenders."
(1 Corinthians 6.9)

"...I tell you the truth, no one can see the kingdom of God unless he is born again."
(John 3.3)

DAY 28

QUESTIONS:

Can you explain what the kingdom of God is, and how one becomes a part of it?

What does the parable of the treasure in the field show about the kingdom?

DAY 28

PRAYER: Thanksgiving

Praise God with great joy! It is an unqualified privilege to be a child of the kingdom.

Put yourself in the shoes of the man who found treasure in the field. How would you thank God?

CONFESSIONS

I am a child of the kingdom, a citizen of God's realm.
I am called to be an ambassador of Christ and I do the will of my Father.

NOTES

What impact has this study had on you? Note other lessons you have learnt from the study.

DAY 29

QUESTIONS:

What about the story of the merchant and the pearl? What can we learn from it?

What did Jesus mean when He spoke of cutting off the right hand and the right leg?

DAY 29

PRAYER:

Ask God for revelation of the kingdom of God and your place in it.

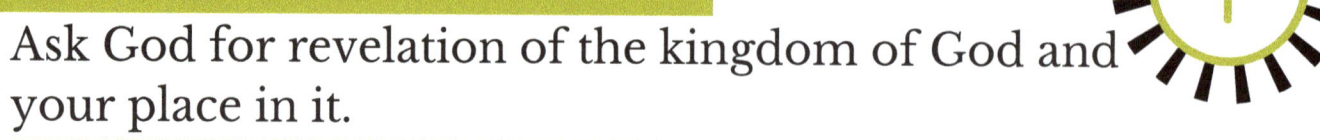

Consecration - Pray to willingly submit your life to the dominion of God.

OTHER PRAYER POINTS

NOTES

What impact has this study had on you? Note other lessons you have learnt from the study.

DAY 30

QUESTIONS:

What are your responsibilities now as an ambassador of the kingdom?

Describe what your lifestyle must be now that you are a child of the kingdom.

DAY 30

PRAYER: Petition

Ask God to help you to represent His message with your words and your life as you ought.

Pray about specific issues in your life that may hinder your effectiveness in the kingdom.

OTHER PRAYER POINTS

NOTES

What impact has this study had on you? Note other lessons you have learnt from the study.

CONCLUSION

But you are a chosen people, a royal priesthood, a holy nation, a people belonging to God, that you may declare the praises of him who called you out of darkness into his wonderful light. Once you were not a people, but now you are the people of God; once you had not received mercy, but now you have received mercy.

1 Peter 2.9-10

Surely there is no end to the goodness of our God. What an inconceivable work of grace He has accomplished! Needless to say, despite all that has been written in the volume and the exercises prepared in this workbook, we have only scratched the surface of the new identity of the believer, as revealed in God's Word.

As you study the Scriptures, you will discover so much more that we can put in a workbook such as this. We all come to this with our own story, and when we are first born again, do not yet see the full picture of this beautiful work of God.

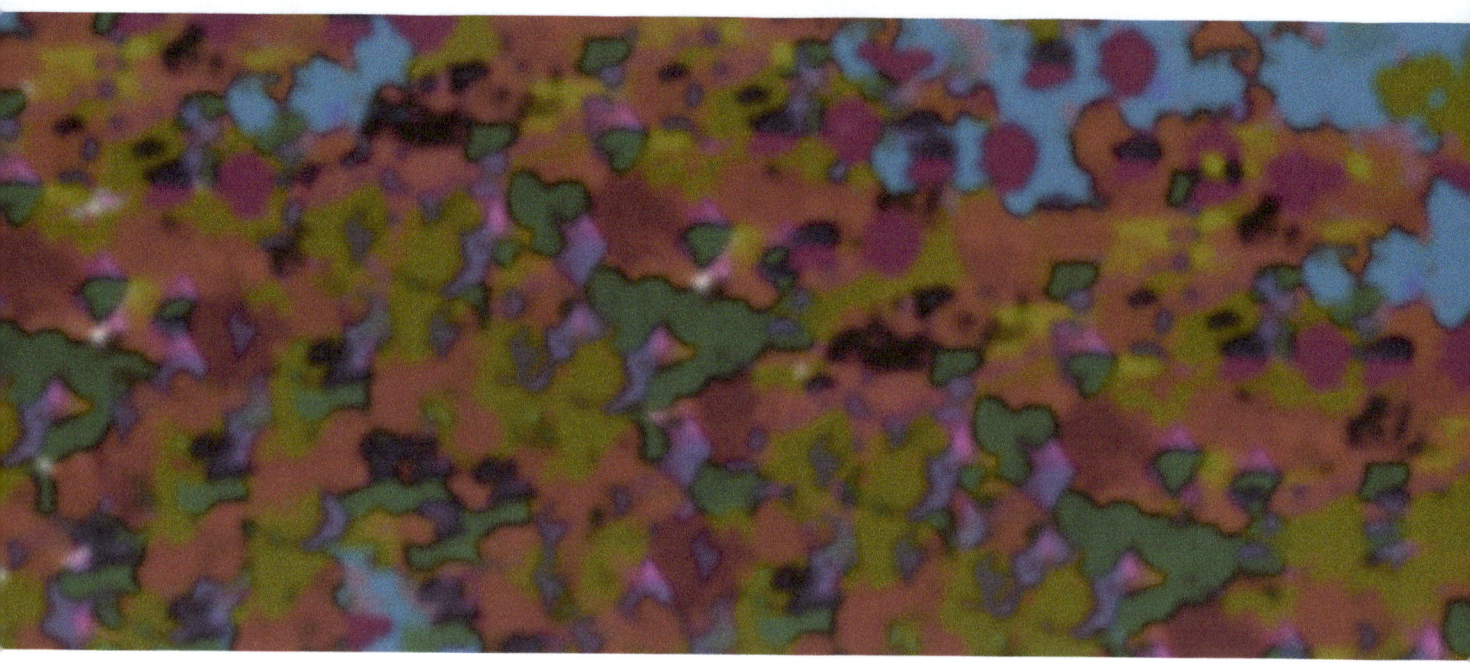

We have stuff that we need to deal with, questions begging for answers, the baggage we need to be divested of, just stuff. A process has begun, a process that will bring these beautiful truths into gradual expression. If you have been doing the exercises prescribed in this workbook, you are already well on the way.

Remember, life in the kingdom is partnering with God for the fulfilment of His purposes in you, for you, and especially through you for His kingdom's sake. If you will embrace the requisite spiritual disciplines as a lifestyle, you will be unstoppable in enjoying and manifesting the life of the kingdom of God.

You may want to pick the follow up , "An Eye To The Crown". It deals with our actions, with lifestyle issues. How do we live after receiving this new identity? I outline the ingredients of this new lifestyle, specific steps and actions that will consolidate you in the faith, give you a beautiful life here and guarantee you a warm welcome into the presence of the Father. It is a total package for victorious living. Shalom!
Please consider leaving a review online so others can find and be blessed by the book.

ABOUT THE AUTHOR

BOLA OGEDENGBE is a lover of God. She is founding pastor of Abba House Church in Paris, France and heads the prophetic ministry 'The Theophilus Company' (La Compagnie Théophile). She speaks five languages and after more than two decades traveling the world as a Conference Interpreter, she moved into full-time ministry and has never looked back.

Her consuming desire is to cover the nations with the gospel. She is a dynamic prophetic minister, teacher, preacher and conference speaker. Her weekly television programme "Passion pour Dieu" reaches a global audience. She is a gifted blogger and writer with several books published and in pre-publication.

Author's blogs
www.bolaoged.com (English)
www.oliviaoged.com (French)
(Subscribe for updates and ebooks)

For ministry, television information
www.compagnietheophile.org (prophetic ministry, conferences, television)
www.abba-house.org (church)

GET THE BOOK.

'We are invited to handle divine treasures which too often elude our comprehension'. REBORN unveils these treasures to us. The book is theologically rich, yet easy to grasp. It is a quick and captivating read. God's goodness shines forth from its pages and it will draw you into a life of peace and victory in God.

Living for eternity

We must live with an eye to eternity and the principles we apply to our lives today will shape our present and our future.

An Eye to the Crown covers ten things you need to do to live a victorious life and win the ultimate prize. these principles will inspire, encourage and empower you for a beautiful lifestyle.

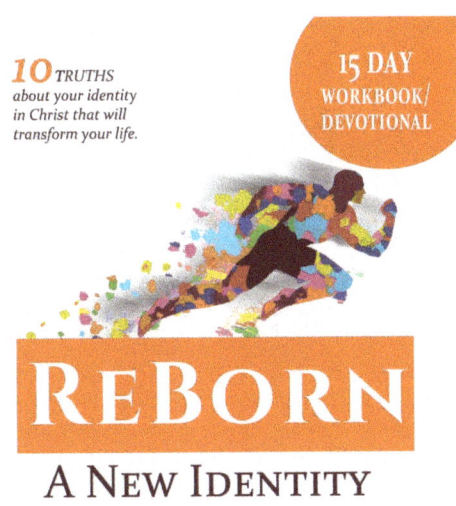

15 DAY DEVOTIONAL

Take a two week challenge into the heart of God's Word on your new identity in Christ. Quotes, questions, points to ponder, journal, prayers - all to guide you for two weeks of deep meditation, revelation and transformation

7 DAY DEVOTIONAL

The shortest of the devotionals, for those with little time albeit big dreams.
In one week you will go through content equivalent to two chapters of the book. You will enjoy a very powerful meditation on the new birth and the unending love of God.

www.ingramcontent.com/pod-product-compliance
Ingram Content Group UK Ltd.
Pitfield, Milton Keynes, MK11 3LW, UK
UKHW060048240426
12048UKWH00012B/669

9 791095 039075